Hey, look gear! I am just so cool!

He also thinks it is cool to play tricks on his pals!

3

His pals feel stupid and are cross with him.

The coach turns to look. There is no fire!

Ha ha! Got you, too! Such fun!

The coach is livid!

He rushes towards his team and tells them.

But they think it is just one of his tricks.

But as they look, a man runs for it! He is soon out of sight.

It's not so much fun **now**, is it Vic?